The Calvin and Hobbes
LAZY SUNDAY BOOK

A Collection of Sunday Calvin and Hobbes Cartoons
by BILL WATTERSON

SCHOLASTIC INC.

New York Toronto London Auckland Sydney

To Rich West

ISBN 0-590-10678-3

12 11 10 9 8 7 6 5 4 3 2 1   7 8 9/9 0 1 2/0

Printed in the U.S.A.   14

First Scholastic printing, September 1997

Calvin and Hobbes is distributed internationally by Universal Press Syndicate.

HMPH.

YES! THE INCREDIBLE SPACEMAN SPIFF SURVIVES! DAZED, BUT UNHURT, OUR HERO CRAWLS FROM THE SMOLDERING WRECKAGE!

SPIFF SETS OFF ACROSS THE PLANET SURFACE. AN OMINOUS, SHADOWY FIGURE FLITS ACROSS A NEARBY HILLTOP! AN ALIEN!

OUR HERO DARTS BEHIND A ROCK AND SETS HIS ZORCHER ON "SHAKE AND BAKE." THE ALIEN APPROACHES!

HI CALVIN! I SEE YOU, SO YOU CAN STOP HIDING NOW! ARE YOU PLAYING COWBOYS OR SOMETHING? CAN I PLAY TOO?

ZOUNDS! THE BOOGER BEING IS IN ALLIANCE WITH THE NAGGON MOTHER SHIP THAT SHOT SPIFF DOWN IN THE FIRST PLACE! OUR HERO OPTS FOR A SPEEDY GETAWAY!

The End.

Calvin and Hobbes by WATTERSON

"BEFORE BEGINNING ANY HOME-PLUMBING REPAIR, MAKE SURE YOU POSSESS THE PROPER TOOLS FOR THE JOB."

"CHECK THE FOLLOWING LIST OF HANDY EXPLETIVES, AND SEE THAT YOU KNOW HOW TO USE THEM."

CALVIN WAKES UP ONE MORNING TO FIND HE NO LONGER EXISTS IN THE THIRD DIMENSION! HE IS **2-D**!

THINNER THAN A SHEET OF PAPER, CALVIN HAS NO SURFACE AREA ON THE BOTTOM OF HIS FEET! HE IS IMMOBILE!

ONLY BY "WAVING" HIS BODY CAN CALVIN CREATE ENOUGH FRICTION WITH THE GROUND TO MOVE!

HAVING WIDTH BUT NO THICKNESS, CALVIN IS VULNERABLE TO THE SLIGHTEST GUST OF WIND!

TO AVOID DRAFTS, HE TWISTS HIMSELF INTO A TUBE, AND ROLLS ACROSS THE FLOOR!

WATTERSON

SOMEONE IS COMING! CALVIN QUICKLY STANDS UP STRAIGHT.

TURNING PERFECTLY SIDEWAYS, HE IS A NEARLY INVISIBLE VERTICAL LINE! NO ONE WILL NOTICE!

HEY DAD, KNOW WHY YOU DIDN'T SEE ME ALL MORNING?? I WAS TWO-DIMENSIONAL!

HMMM, I'LL BET YOU CAN'T DO IT ALL AFTERNOON, TOO...

DEAR!

I'M GOING OUTSIDE, MOM!

HOLD ALL MY CALLS.

CALVIN LOOKS AROUND. SOMETHING IS DIFFERENT.

THE ODD-COLORED TREE BEHIND HIM SLOWLY LIFTS UP! IT'S NOT A TREE AT ALL! IT'S A LEG!

OH NO! CALVIN IS THE SIZE OF A BUG *TO* A BUG! HE RUNS FOR HIS LIFE!

A CLAW CRASHES WITH DEAFENING IMPACT! THE BUG IS TRYING TO STEP ON CALVIN! WHAT A HORRIBLE FATE!

CALVIN SCRAMBLES MADLY, PROMISING HIMSELF THAT HE'LL NEVER SQUISH ANOTHER BUG IF HE LIVES TO RETURN TO NORMAL SIZE!

SUDDENLY IN A SPRAY OF SLIME, THE BUG IS GONE! A MONSTROUS FROG LICKS ITS CHOPS! CALVIN IS SAVED!

AACCK! WHAT'S THAT ON MY PLATE?! GOOD HEAVENS, GET IT OFF THE TABLE.!!

BUT MOM, FROGS ARE OUR *FRIENDS!*

Calvin and Hobbes

by WATTERSON

OH BOY OH BOY OH BOY OH BOY OH BOY OH BOY OH BOY OH BOY OH BOY OH BOY

WAIT! WAIT! I'VE GOT TO SAVOR THIS MOMENT! THE BRILLIANCE OF IT ALL! I'M A GENIUS! A SHEER *GENIUS!*

SUSIE'S PLAYING ON THE SIDEWALK! NOW'S MY CHANCE TO USE THE SNOWBALL I'VE BEEN SAVING IN THE FREEZER!

SHE'LL NEVER EXPECT A SNOWBALL IN *JUNE!* BOY, WILL SHE BE MAD! HA HA HA!

THIS IS GOING TO BE GREAT! HERE IT COMES! OH BOY! OH BOY!

HEY SUSIE!!

PIFF

I *MISSED!* DARN IT DARN IT DARN IT!! OF ALL THE MISERABLE LUCK! AAARRGHH!

THERE MUST'VE BEEN A CROSS BREEZE! I CAN'T BELIEVE IT! I SAVED THAT SNOWBALL FOR THREE WHOLE MONTHS! I...

SCOOP SCOOP

I.. I... UH...

POW

THE IRONY OF THIS IS JUST SICKENING.

THE DREADED SCUM BEINGS FIRE! SPACEMAN SPIFF IS *HIT!*

IT NEVER FAILS. I JUST WASHED AND WAXED THIS THING.

OUR HERO, THE INTREPID SPACEMAN SPIFF, STRUGGLES WITH THE CONTROLS OF HIS DAMAGED SPACECRAFT!

THE FREEM PROPULSION BLASTERS ARE USELESS! SPIFF CRASHES ONTO THE SURFACE OF AN ALIEN PLANET!

UNSCATHED, THE FEARLESS SPACE EXPLORER EMERGES FROM THE SMOLDERING WRECKAGE! HE IS MAROONED ON A HOSTILE WORLD!

SCORCHED BY TWIN SUNS, THE PLANET IS NOTHING BUT BARREN ROCK AND METHANE! THERE'S NO HOPE OF FINDING FOOD OR WATER!

SPIFF COLLAPSES! OH NO, A HIDEOUS ALIEN SPOTS HIM! IN HIS WEAKENED STATE, SPIFF IS NO MATCH FOR THE MONSTER! *THIS COULD BE THE END!!*

LUNCHTIME! I BROUGHT YOU A SANDWICH AND SOME LEMONADE.

BRING THE DISHES BACK WHEN YOU'RE DONE, OK?

...OH WELL.

THANKS, MOM.

22

THE FIRE'S NOT LIGHTING, HUH? CAN I MAKE A SUGGESTION?

GIVE UP ON THAT SISSY LIGHTER FLUID.

CAN'T WE COOK THE HAMBURGERS YET?

THE COALS AREN'T HOT ENOUGH.

BUT I'M HUNGRY! I WANT TO EAT **NOW!**

WELL, YOU'LL JUST HAVE TO WAIT.

YOU KNOW, CALVIN, SOMETIMES THE ANTICIPATION OF SOMETHING IS MORE FUN THAN THE THING ITSELF ONCE YOU GET IT.

HERE WE ARE, IT'S A BEAUTIFUL EVENING. IT'S NICE TO JUST SIT HERE AND LOOK AT THE TREES WHILE WE WAIT FOR THE COALS TO GET HOT, DON'T YOU THINK?

DINNER WILL BE OVER SOON, AND AFTERWARD WE'LL BE DISTRACTED WITH OTHER THINGS TO DO. BUT NOW WE HAVE A FEW MINUTES TO OURSELVES TO ENJOY THE EVENING.

THESE SUMMER DAYS GO BY SO QUICKLY. IT'S GOOD THAT EVERY NOW AND THEN WE HAVE TO WAIT FOR SOMETHING.

SO SHOULD I GO TO McDONALD'S THEN, OR WHAT?

YEAH, I KNOW. YOU THINK YOU'RE GOING TO BE SIX ALL YOUR LIFE.

CALVIN AND HOBBES
by WATTERSON

THAT RUN DOESN'T COUNT! YOU DIDN'T TOUCH THIRD BASE!

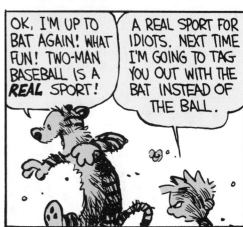

27

 Calvin and Hobbes by WATTERSON

 AH-CHOO!

 *WHEN* ... NO BRAINS.

 AH.. AH.. AH.. AH

 CHOOO!!

 THE FORCE OF THE NASAL EXPLOSION SENDS CALVIN REELING THROUGH THE STRATOSPHERE!

 WITH LESS AND LESS AIR TO RESIST HIS MOMENTUM, HE BREAKS THE PULL OF EARTH'S GRAVITY AND HURLS PAST THE MOON!

 AS HE PASSES OUT OF THE GALAXY, CALVIN REFLECTS ON THE WISDOM OF COVERING ONE'S MOUTH WHEN SNEEZING TO DEFLECT THE PROPULSION.

 ALAS, IT IS KNOWLEDGE GAINED TOO LATE FOR POOR CALVIN, THE HUMAN SATELLITE! ...BUT WAIT! ANOTHER SNEEZE IS BREWING! CALVIN TURNS HIMSELF AROUND!

 THE SECOND SNEEZE ROCKETS HIM BACK TO EARTH! HE'S SAVED! IT'S A MIRACLE!

 AH CHOO! GOD BLESS YOU. OH, HE DOES, MOM, HE DOES.

CalviN and HObbEs

by WATTERSON

Calvin and Hobbes

by WATTERSON

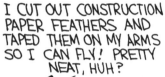

WIPE THAT GRIN OFF YOUR FACE!

WELL, HOBBES, HOW DO I LOOK?

I'M DOING MY BEST TO BITE MY TONGUE.

I CUT OUT CONSTRUCTION PAPER FEATHERS AND TAPED THEM ON MY ARMS SO I CAN FLY! PRETTY NEAT, HUH?

IF PAPER FEATHERS ARE ALL IT TAKES TO FLY, DON'T YOU THINK WE'D HAVE HEARD ABOUT IT BEFORE?

IT TAKES AN UNCOMMON MIND TO THINK OF THESE THINGS, HOBBES.

I'D AGREE WITH THAT.

HERE'S A GORGE. THIS IS A GOOD SPOT.

YOU'RE GOING TO JUMP OFF THIS LEDGE?

HECK NO! I NEED *MOMENTUM*! I WANT YOU TO *TOSS* ME OVER.

YOU UNDERSTAND I ASSUME NO RESPONSIBILITY FOR THIS?

RIGHT. *I* GET THE PATENT.

HEAVE!

I'M FLYING! I'M FLYING!

I'M..... UH OH... I

DON'T SELL THE BIKE SHOP, ORVILLE.

SHUT UP AND GO GET ME SOME ANTISEPTIC.

32

Calvin and Hobbes by WATTERSON

POW!

PANT WHEEZE GASP

WELL, IF YOU DIDN'T GET IN A FIGHT AT SCHOOL, WHAT ON EARTH HAPPENED TO YOU?!

LET'S JUST SAY SOMETIMES I WISH I HAD A GERBIL.

35

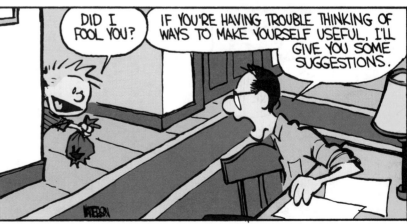

CALVIN AND HOBBES

by WATERSON

CALVIN and HOBBES by WATTERSON

First there was nothing...

...then there was Calvin!

Calvin, the mighty god, creates the universe with pure will!

From utter nothingness comes swirling form! Life begins where once was void!

But Calvin is no kind and loving god! He's one of the old gods! He demands sacrifice!

Yes, Calvin is a god of the underworld! And the puny inhabitants of earth displease him!

The great Calvin ignores their pleas for mercy and the doomed writhe in agony!

HAVE YOU SEEN HOW ABSORBED CALVIN IS WITH THOSE TINKERTOYS? HE'S CREATING WHOLE WORLDS OVER THERE!

I'LL BET HE GROWS UP TO BE AN ARCHITECT.

Calvin and Hobbes
by WATTERSON

CaLviN and HobbES

by WATTERSON

HERE'S A BOX OF CRAYONS. I NEED SOME ILLUSTRATIONS FOR A STORY I'M WRITING.

YOU CAN DRAW SOMETHING BESIDES TIGERS, CAN'T YOU?

SURE. LEOPARDS, PUMAS, OCELOTS.. ..YOU NAME IT.

HERE, DAD, READ *THIS* STORY TONIGHT. I WROTE IT AND HOBBES ILLUSTRATED IT.

..UM.... OK.

"THE DAD WHO LIVED TO REGRET BEING MEAN TO HIS KID."

WHAT ARE YOU PAUSING FOR? KEEP READING.

Barney's dad was really bad,
So Barney hatched a plan.
When his dad said, "Eat your peas!"
Barney shouted, "NO!" and ran.

peas

Barney

Barney tricked his mean ol' dad,
And locked him in the cellar.
His mom never found out
where he'd gone,
'Cause Barney didn't tell her.

door

key

There his dad spent his life,
Eating mice and gruel.
With every bite for fifty years
He was sorry he'd been cruel.
THE END.

Barney's dad

mice

YOU KNOW HOW A LOT OF STORIES HAVE MORALS TO THEM...?

I *GET* IT, I *GET* IT!

WATTERSON & HOBS

45

Calvin and Hobbes

by WATTERSON

CALVIN and HOBBES

by WATTERSON

THE LATE CRETACEOUS PERIOD...
WHEN DINOSAURS RULED THE EARTH!

..AND CALVIN RULED THE DINOSAURS!

THE TERRIBLE TYRANNOSAURUS SINKS ITS TEETH INTO A TRICERATOPS!

TRIUMPHANT AGAIN, THE UNDISPUTED KING OF DINOSAURS LETS OUT A MIGHTY ROAR!

WITH SAVAGE FEROCITY, THE MONSTER BEGINS ITS FEAST! LIMB-SEVERING, BONE-CRUNCHING AND TENDON-SNAPPING, HE...

CALVIN! THAT'S DISGUSTING!

FOR HEAVEN'S SAKE, SLOW DOWN AND CHEW QUIETLY!

THE TERRIBLE TYRANNOSAURUS RESUMES EATING, MORTIFIED THAT SOMEONE MIGHT SEE HIM.

CALVIN AND HOBBES by WATTERSON

A VOICE CACKLES IN CALVIN'S RADIO. "ENEMY FIGHTERS AT TWO O'CLOCK!"

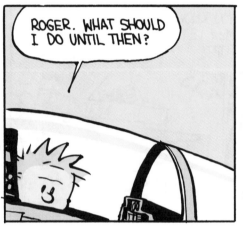

ROGER. WHAT SHOULD I DO UNTIL THEN?

CALVIN'S F-4 PHANTOM SCREAMS ACROSS THE SKY!

BUT WHAT'S THIS? THE CANOPY GLASS IS ALL SMEARED! HE CAN HARDLY SEE THROUGH IT!

OH, NO! THE THROTTLE SNAPS OFF IN HIS HAND!

CALVIN'S ONLY HOPE IS TO LAND, BUT THE WHEELS REFUSE TO OPEN! THEY'RE STUCK!

FRANTICALLY CALVIN TRIES TO EJECT, BUT THE COCKPIT IS FUSED TOGETHER! HIS JET IS A HOPELESS MESS! EVERYTHING IS GOING WRONG!

STUPID MODEL.

CALVIN and HOBBES

by WATTERSON

C'MON, HOBBES. LET ME UP INTO THE TREE FORT.

SAY THE PASSWORD.

NO! YOU KNOW IT'S ME! LET ME UP!

YOU MAY BE SOME OTHER KID IN DISGUISE.

IT'S *ME*, CALVIN! LET ME UP, YOU HAIRBALL BARFER!

AN INSULT! WELL, YOU CAN JUST STAY DOWN THERE *FOREVER*, MR. STINKER.

OH, NO! HERE COMES SUSIE! LET ME UP QUICK, SO WE CAN THROW THINGS AT HER! HURRY! LET DOWN THE ROPE!

LA DE DA DUM DOO ♪♫

SHE'S COMING! QUICK! LET DOWN THE ROPE! I'M SORRY I INSULTED YOU! OK? SEE, I SAID I WAS SORRY! CAN'T YOU LET DOWN THE ROPE?!

YOU HAVE TO SAY THE PASSWORD.

..Verse Seven: TIGERS ARE PERFECT, THE *E*-PIT-O-ME OF GOOD LOOKS AND GRACE AND QUIET..UH..UM..DIGNITY.

I WAS GOING TO ASK YOU TO COME OVER AND PLAY HOUSE, BUT I THINK YOU'D BE A WEIRD EXAMPLE FOR OUR CHILDREN.

ONE OF THESE DAYS I'M GOING TO MAKE YOU INTO A RUG! YOU HEAR ME?? A RUG!

Calvin and Hobbes by WATTERSON

THE CALL GOES OUT! WE'RE ON THE MOVE!

UP THROUGH THE WINDING MAZE! FASTER! FASTER!

CALVIN SCRAMBLES UP THE GRAINY TUNNEL!

OUT HE POPS INTO THE BLINDING SUN! CALVIN THE ANT RUSHES DOWN THE HILL TO THE BRICK WALK!

OTHER ANTS RUSH AROUND HIM IN THEIR MAD HURRY! CALVIN TRIES TO KEEP UP!

AT LAST HE REACHES THE MONSTROUS DEAD CATERPILLAR! WITHOUT PAUSING, HE HOISTS IT UP!

THE QUEEN DEMANDS HIS TIRELESS TOIL! CALVIN IS BACK OFF TO THE ANT-HILL AS FAST AS HE CAN GO!

WORK, WORK, WORK! THAT'S ALL I'M GOOD FOR AROUND HERE!

I HARDLY THINK PICKING UP YOUR ROOM ONCE IN A WHILE QUALIFIES YOU AS A SLAVE.

CALVIN and HObbEs

by WATTERSON

THIS IS CALVIN, YOUR CAPTAIN, SPEAKING...

...JUST TO REASSURE YOU THAT, YES, THERE IS SOMEONE UP FRONT.

CALVIN PILOTS THE JET AIRLINER ACROSS THE COUNTRY AT 35,000 FEET.

HE IS GIVEN CLEARANCE TO LAND. BUT WHAT'S THIS? A PLANE FROM A RIVAL AIRLINE IS MAKING FOR THE SAME RUNWAY TO SHAVE PRECIOUS MINUTES OFF ITS SCHEDULE!

IT'S A 600-MPH GAME OF CHICKEN! CALVIN PULLS BACK ON THE THROTTLE AND LURCHES AHEAD!

THE OTHER PILOT TRIES TO CUT CALVIN OFF WITH A SUDDEN DROP IN ALTITUDE!

CALVIN SWITCHES ON THE "FASTEN SEAT BELT" LIGHT IN THE CABIN, AND DOES A BARREL ROLL!

AT 5 Gs, CALVIN HOPES NOT TO BLACK OUT!

AS THEY CLOSE IN ON THE RUNWAY, THE OTHER PILOT HAS NO CHOICE BUT TO PULL UP AND CIRCLE AROUND AGAIN! CALVIN WINS!

HEY, MOM, IS IT TRUE I COULD GET A PILOT'S LICENSE AT AGE 14?

NO.

CALVIN and HOBBES by WATTERSON

zzzzzzzzzzzzz

FILTH! CONTAMINATION! PESTILENCE! HA HA HA!

OF ALL LIVING CREATURES, FEW ARE MORE REPULSIVE THAN CALVIN THE BUG!

HE EXISTS ONLY TO SUCK BLOOD AND TRANSMIT PARASITIC DISEASE!

SEARCHING FOR SOMEONE TO INFECT, CALVIN FLIES LOW OVER THE PICNIC TABLE!

Tom
INGREDIENTS: SALT,

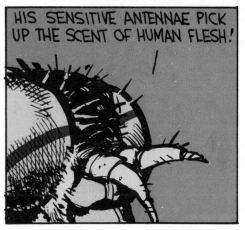
HIS SENSITIVE ANTENNAE PICK UP THE SCENT OF HUMAN FLESH!

TOUCHING DOWN, CALVIN INSERTS HIS NEEDLELIKE PROBOSCIS INTO A VEIN! PROTOZOANS IN HIS SALIVA QUICKLY INDUCE PLAGUE!

WILL YOU STOP THAT AWFUL SLURPING?! YOU'RE MAKING ME SICK!

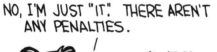

Calvin and Hobbes
by WATTERSON

SPACEMAN SPIFF EXPLORES THE OUTERMOST REACHES OF THE UNIVERSE.

BY POPULAR REQUEST.

INTREPID EXPLORER SPACEMAN SPIFF LANDS ON AN UNCHARTED PLANET. WHAT STRANGE WONDERS WILL HE DISCOVER HERE?

SPIFF SETS OUT IN SEARCH OF SENTIENT LIFE!

WHAT A STRANGE PLANET THIS IS! ITS SURFACE IS SURPRISINGLY SOFT AND POROUS!

AND HERE CURIOUS GEYSERS BLAST HOT AIR!

SUDDENLY IT DAWNS ON HIM! SPIFF IS NOT ON THE PLANET'S SURFACE AT ALL! HE'S WALKING ON A RECLINING ALIEN!!

OUR HERO SETS HIS DEATH RAY BLASTER.

ZZ.. MMF HM?

71

73

Calvin and Hobbes
by WATTERSON

calvin and hobbes by WATERSON

DINOSAURS EVERYWHERE FLEE FOR THEIR LIVES!

CALVIN IS COMING!

THE LATE CRETACEOUS: THE LAST EPOCH OF THE MIGHTY DINOSAURS!

KING OF THE THUNDER LIZARDS IS THE FEARSOME CALVIN, THE TYRANNOSAURUS!

SEVEN TONS OF MUSCLE AND TEETH, HE SEARCHES FOR PREY!

CALVIN, FOR GOODNESS' SAKE, STOP STOMPING AROUND! YOU'RE DRIVING ME CRAZY!

OW!! CHOMP!

HOW DID THE FEARSOME TYRANNOSAURUS BECOME EXTINCT? NOW WE KNOW!

WATTERSON

Calvin and Hobbes

by WATTERSON

SCHOOL'S OUT! FREE AT LAST!

AND JUST SIX PRECIOUS HOURS BEFORE BED TO FORGET EVERYTHING I LEARNED TODAY.

I HATE COMING HOME FROM SCHOOL. I NEVER KNOW IF HOBBES IS WAITING TO POUNCE ON ME.

MAYBE I CAN STAND OFF TO THE SIDE HERE, AND PUSH THE DOOR OPEN WITH A STICK.

I'M HOME!

WHAT DO YOU DO, WAIT UNTIL YOU SEE THE WHITES OF MY EYES?!?

BOY, YOU SHOULD'VE *SEEN* THEM! THEY WERE AS BIG AS DINNER PLATES! HOO HOO HOO!

Calvin and Hobbes
by WATTERSON

81

CALVIN and HOBBES

by WATTERSON

Galvin and Hobbes

by WATTERSON

THE VALIANT SPACEMAN SPIFF, INTERGALACTIC EXPLORER, COMES IN OVER THE MOUNTAINS OF A STRANGE PLANET!

OUR HERO DESPERATELY HOPES TO FIND A REST AREA WITH WORKING FACILITIES.

SPACEMAN SPIFF LANDS ON THE DISTANT PLANET ZOKK!

CLIMBING DOWN FROM HIS SPACECRAFT, OUR HERO PREPARES TO EXPLORE THE SURFACE!

UNEXPECTEDLY, SPIFF'S FIRST STEP SENDS HIM CAREENING THROUGH THE SKY!

SPIFF QUICKLY REALIZES THAT PLANET ZOKK HAS ONLY A FRACTION OF EARTH'S GRAVITY!

OOF

WITH PRACTICE, OUR HERO SOON FINDS HE CAN BOUND EFFORTLESSLY ACROSS THE LANDSCAPE!

WATTERSON

STOP BOUNCING ON THE BED AND GO TO SLEEP!

calvin and hobbes

by WATTERSON

Calvin and Hobbes
by WATTERSON

IF *I* WAS IN CHARGE, WE'D NEVER SEE GRASS BETWEEN OCTOBER AND MAY.

ON "THREE", READY? ONE... TWO... THREE!

SNOW!

I SAID SNOW! C'MON! SNOW!

SNOW!

OK THEN, *DON'T* SNOW! SEE WHAT *I* CARE! I *LIKE* THIS WEATHER! LET'S HAVE IT FOREVER!

PLEEAASE SNOW! PLEASE?? JUST A FOOT! OK, EIGHT INCHES! THAT'S ALL! C'MON! SIX INCHES, EVEN! HOW ABOUT JUST SIX??

I'M *WAAIIITING*...

RRRRGGHHH

DO YOU WANT ME TO BECOME AN ATHEIST?

91

Calvin and Hobbes
by WATTERSON

AHH... THE PERFECT SLUSHBALL!

HARD ENOUGH TO STING, YET SLOPPY ENOUGH TO DRIBBLE DOWN THE COLLAR AND SOAK THE UNDERGARMENTS.

HERE COMES SUSIE! NOW'S MY CHANCE TO HIT HER WITH A SLUSHBALL!

I SEE YOU! YOU'D BETTER NOT THROW THAT! SANTA CLAUS IS WATCHING YOU RIGHT NOW!

ZINGG FWISSHHH!

WHAP!

OH YES! YES! IT WAS WORTH IT! WHAT A SHOT! I'M NOT SORRY! OH, IT WAS BEAUTIFUL! I'D DO IT AGAIN IN A MINUTE! HA HA!

SANTA'S GONNA SKIP THIS BLOCK FOR YEARS.

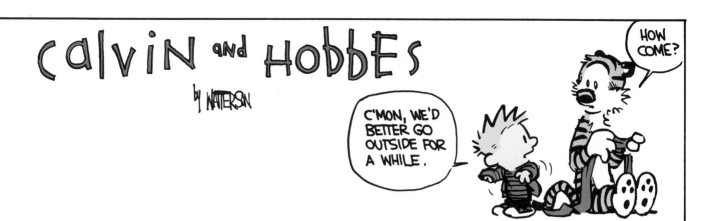

OK, LET'S SEE... IF THE WIND IS BLOWING NORTH-NORTHEAST AT 6 MPH, AND I THROW THE SNOWBALL DUE WEST AT 90 MPH WITH A SLIGHT TOP SPIN....

HA! SUSIE DIDN'T EVEN HEAR ME SNEAK UP!

NOW I'LL CREAM HER CRANIUM WITH A BARRAGE OF SNOWBALLS!

WHIZZZ

PIFF

PIFF

THESE DARN CROSS BREEZES! SHE DIDN'T EVEN NOTICE!

YOU'RE THE WORST SHOT IN THE WORLD, CALVIN! IF IT WASN'T FOR GRAVITY, YOU PROBABLY COULDN'T EVEN HIT THE GROUND!

SMACK!

I DID IT! I DID IT! JUST WHEN IT REALLY COUNTED, I *DID* IT! HA HA HA! RIGHT IN THE KISSER! HA HA!

BAD NEWS, MOM. I PROMISED MY SOUL TO THE DEVIL THIS AFTERNOON.

OH? THAT RECENTLY?

CALVIN and HOBBES by WATTERSON

CLUMP

THE PTERANODON SPREADS HIS GIANT WINGS, AND..

CALVIN AND HOBBES by WATTERSON

I CAN NEVER ENJOY SUNDAYS, BECAUSE IN THE BACK OF MY MIND I ALWAYS KNOW I'VE GOT TO GO TO SCHOOL THE NEXT DAY.

IT'S LIKE TRYING TO ENJOY YOUR LAST MEAL BEFORE THE EXECUTION.

A PENNY FOR YOUR THOUGHTS.

SORRY. *MY* THOUGHTS ARE A BUCK APIECE.

A DOLLAR?! THAT'S OUTRAGEOUS! YOUR THOUGHTS AREN'T WORTH THAT!

THIS ONE IS! AT A DOLLAR, IT'S THE BARGAIN OF A LIFETIME.

I WOULDN'T PAY A NICKLE FOR ANY THOUGHT YOU'VE EVER HAD IN YOUR WHOLE FLEA-RIDDEN EXISTENCE!

THAT LITTLE REMARK JUST MADE THE PRICE *TEN* DOLLARS!

TEN?? YOU CAN'T EXTORT ME! *KEEP* YOUR STUPID THOUGHT!

IF YOU KNEW WHAT IT WAS, YOU'D *BEG* TO PAY TEN BUCKS FOR IT.

C'MON, JUST TELL ME WHAT IT IS, WILL YOU?

NOTHING DOING, PAL.

OK, OK! I'LL GIVE YOU 25 CENTS. THAT'S ALL I HAVE.

LET'S SEE IT.

HERE! 25 CENTS! NOW WHAT'S THIS BIG, EXPENSIVE THOUGHT OF YOURS?!

"A FOOL AND HIS MONEY ARE SOON PAR..."

WATTERSON

105

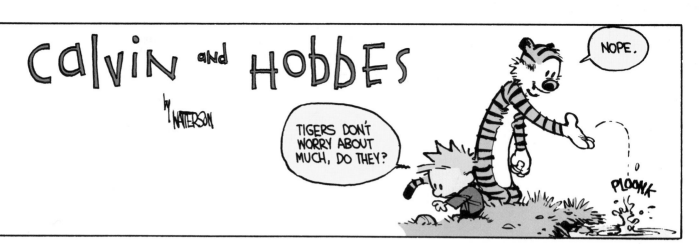

106

CalviN and HobbEs

by WATTERSON

SIGHHHHHH..

WHAP

SIGHHHHHH..

CalviN and HobbEs
by WATTERSON

GET UP, CALVIN! I'M NOT GOING TO CALL YOU AGAIN!

I BET.
. . .

YOU'RE GOING TO MISS THE BUS! NOW GET OUT OF BED!

YOU DON'T KNOW THE ANSWER? THEN SIT DOWN.

$\begin{array}{r} 12 \\ -7 \end{array}$

Hey, Twinky, want to see if there's an afterlife?

NO, YOU CAN'T GO PLAY UNTIL YOU FINISH YOUR HOMEWORK.

JUST EAT YOUR FOOD. YOU DON'T NEED TO PLAY WITH IT.

STOP STALLING AND GET IN THE BATHTUB.

NO, YOU CAN'T STAY UP A LITTLE LONGER. GO TO BED.

HAVE A GOOD NIGHT'S SLEEP. TOMORROW'S ANOTHER BIG DAY!

...SIGHHHHHH...

calvin and Hobbes
by WATTERSON

TRUE FRIENDS ARE HARD TO COME BY.

I NEED MORE MONEY.

I WISH PEOPLE WERE MORE LIKE ANIMALS.

ANIMALS DON'T TRY TO CHANGE YOU OR MAKE YOU FIT IN. THEY JUST ENJOY THE PLEASURE OF YOUR COMPANY.

ANIMALS AREN'T CONDITIONAL ABOUT FRIENDSHIPS. ANIMALS LIKE YOU JUST THE WAY YOU ARE.

THEY LISTEN TO YOUR PROBLEMS, THEY COMFORT YOU WHEN YOU'RE SAD, AND ALL THEY ASK IN RETURN IS A LITTLE KINDNESS.

WHOOONK! *SOB* IT'S SO...SO *TRUE*! HOOOOT! THBPBTPTH!

...AND SPEAKING OF "A LITTLE KINDNESS," I'D HAVE A TUNA FISH SANDWICH ANY TIME SOON THAT YOU HAPPEN TO MAKE ONE...

OF COURSE, *SOME* ANIMALS GET ON YOUR NERVES ONCE IN A WHILE.

WATTERSON

CalviN and HobbEs

by WATTERSON

MILD-MANNERED CALVIN IS STUCK INSIDE DOING MATH PROBLEMS ON A BEAUTIFUL SUNDAY.

NO ONE IS WATCHING! HE DASHES INTO HIS CLOSET! *THIS* IS A JOB FOR...

STUPENDOUS MAN!

DEFENDER OF FREEDOM! ADVOCATE OF LIBERTY!

A BRIGHT CRIMSON STREAK BLASTS UP THROUGH THE ATMOSPHERE, AND THEN TURNS BACK TOWARD EARTH!

GAINING STUPENDOUS MOMENTUM, *STUPENDOUS MAN* STRIKES THE GROUND AT AN ACUTE ANGLE WITH STUPENDOUS FORCE!

THE EARTH SLOWLY STOPS ROTATING... AND BEGINS TO TURN IN THE OPPOSITE DIRECTION!

PUSHING WITH ALL HIS MIGHT, *STUPENDOUS MAN* TURNS THE PLANET ALL THE WAY AROUND BACKWARD! THE SUN SETS IN THE EAST AND RISES IN THE WEST! SOON IT'S 10 A.M. THE PREVIOUS DAY!

WHAT ARE YOU DOING OUTSIDE? DID YOU FINISH YOUR HOMEWORK ALREADY?

IT'S SATURDAY! I DON'T NEED TO DO IT UNTIL TOMORROW... THANKS TO *STUPENDOUS MAN!*

calvin and Hobbes
by Watterson

118

YOU CAN TAKE THE TIGER OUT OF THE JUNGLE, BUT YOU CAN'T TAKE THE JUNGLE OUT OF THE TIGER!

THE QUESTION *IS*, HOW CAN YOU GET THE TIGER *BACK* IN THE JUNGLE?

CalviN aNd HobbEs

by WATTERSON

DO RE MI FA SO LA TI DO

A SPARROW ALIGHTS UPON A TREE BRANCH.

BUT THIS IS NO *ORDINARY* SPARROW! THIS IS A *SONG* SPARROW!

SWAYING GENTLY IN THE BREEZE, HE PREPARES TO BURST FORTH IN RAPTUROUS MELODY!

ON TOP OF SPA-GHETTI

ALL COVERED WITH CHEEEESE, I LOST MY POOR MEEEATBALL, WHEN...

calviN and HobbEs by WATTERSON

CALVIN and HOBBES

by WATTERSON

CLICK

UH OH...

THE SKY IS A DEEP ORANGE! CALVIN'S SKIN IS A PALE GREEN! YELLOW FLOWERS ARE NOW BLUE!

EVERY COLOR IS THE OPPOSITE OF WHAT IT SHOULD BE!

CALVIN HAS BEEN TRANSFERRED TO A COLOR FILM NEGATIVE!

HIS ONLY HOPE IS TO BE PROCESSED BY A 1-HOUR PHOTO FINISHER! DEVELOPER! I NEED DEVELOPER!

DOGGONE IT, CALVIN! THAT'S *ANOTHER* PICTURE RUINED! CAN'T YOU LOOK PLEASANT FOR 1/500TH OF A SECOND?!

AFTERWORD

Long ago the Sunday comics were printed the size of an entire newspaper page. Each comic was like a color poster. Not surprisingly, with all that space to fill, cartoonists produced works of incredible beauty and power that we just don't see anymore, now that strips are a third or a quarter of their former size. Whereas Little Nemo could dream through 15 surreal panels back in the early part of the century, today it's rare to see a Sunday strip with more than six panels—especially if the characters move. All the things that make comics fun to read—the stories, the dialogue, the pictures—have gotten simpler and simpler in order to keep the work legible at smaller and smaller sizes. The art form has been in a process of retrograde evolution for decades. For those of us trying to return some of the childhood fun we had marveling at comic drawings, the opportunities today are discouraging.

Cartoons can be much more than we've been seeing lately. How much more will depend on what newspaper readers will demand. One thing, though, is certain: little boys, like tigers, will roam all the territory they can get.

—BILL WATTERSON

The End